THE
Archive Photographs
SERIES

BOULTON PAUL
AIRCRAFT

Three Boulton Paul test pilots relaxing by a Defiant night fighter in 1941. Left to right: Robin Lindsay Neale, Chief Test Pilot Fl. Lt. Cecil Feather and Colin Evans.

THE
Archive Photographs
SERIES

BOULTON PAUL
AIRCRAFT

Compiled by
The Boulton Paul Association

CHALFORD

First published 1996
Copyright © The Boulton Paul Association, 1996

The Chalford Publishing Company
St Mary's Mill, Chalford,
Stroud, Gloucestershire, GL6 8NX

ISBN 0 7524 0625 6

Typesetting and origination by
The Chalford Publishing Company
Printed in Great Britain by
Redwood Books, Trowbridge

This book is dedicated to the memory of
John A. Chambers
an employee of Boulton Paul Aircraft for 47 years
and founder member and first Chairman of the
Boulton Paul Association

Front cover:
The Boulton & Paul P.8 Atlantic being built in February 1919
for an attempt on the first Transatlantic flight.
Just behind is the second P.7 Bourges, F2904, after its Mousehold crash.

Contents

Acknowledgements

We have to thank Dowty Boulton Paul Ltd for the use of most of the photographs in this book, which come from their archives. The vast majority, in the region of 240, have never been seen in print before. Other photographs come from members of the Boulton Paul Association and Dowty Boulton Paul employees including:

Mark Ansell, Alec Brew, John Chambers, Roger Hart, Brian Holmes, J.D. North, Colin Penny, Dave Plant.

Details of the Boulton Paul Association are available from:

The Secretary,
35, Blakeley Avenue,
Wolverhampton,
WV6 9HR.

VIEW OF AIRCRAFT WORKS FROM AN AEROPLANE.

A re-touched aerial view of Boulton & Paul's Riverside aircraft works, Norwich, during the First World War.

Introduction

Boulton Paul Aircraft has been in the aircraft industry for over eighty years, and in that time has changed its name on three occasions. It began in 1915 as the aircraft department of Boulton & Paul Ltd, a well-established Norwich company, but in 1934 the aircraft department was sold off and became an independent company, Boulton Paul Aircraft Ltd, moving to Wolverhampton in 1936. In 1961 it merged with the Dowty Group to become Dowty Boulton Paul Ltd, beginning to trade as Dowty Aerospace Wolverhampton in 1991.

Its former parent, Boulton & Paul Ltd, is actually 200 years old, and went through several name changes in its own development. It was founded as an ironmongers in Cockey Lane, Norwich in 1797 by William Moore. Through the nineteenth century it became an ironmongers, woodworker and steel erector, with successive name changes as first William Staples Boulton and then John Joseph Dawson Paul became associated with the company.

By 1914 it was a large diversified concern most widely known for its pre-fabricated wooden buildings, but also produced an astonishing array of products from cast-iron manure carts to motor-boat engines. In 1915 the Government awarded Boulton & Paul their first contract to build aircraft with an order for fifty No. FE. 2Bs, the first flying on 4th October 1915. A total of 250 No were built, followed by 300 of the Rolls-Royce Eagle-powered FE. 2Ds.

In August 1917 they received their first order for Sopwith Camels and went on to build 1,575 in all, the largest number by any manufacturer. The aircraft were built in the company's Riverside Works in Norwich, but they helped develop an airfield on Mousehold Heath to the East of the city on which to test the aircraft.

With the average of twenty eight Camels being built per month, the company decided to create their own aircraft design department, and as Chief Engineer recruited John Dudley North. J.D. North as he is usually known, had begun work with Horatio Barber at Hendon in 1911, but when the company closed he went to work next door as Chief Engineer of the Grahame White Co., though only twenty years old.

After the start of the War he moved to Austin Motors as superintendent of production, setting up the manufacture of the RE.7 and RE.8. While there he initiated the design of the Austin-Ball Scout, to the ideas of Albert Ball, and also featuring machine guns on a moveable mounting.

Having moved to Boulton & Paul he set about the design of a Sopwith Camel replacement with some urgency. A large number of other manufacturers were also interested in this requirement, and North received prototype orders for two designs, the P.3 and P.5, though the latter was eventually cancelled. One example of the P.3 Bobolink, (named after an American bird) was ordered, but lost out on a fly-off of competing designs to the Sopwith Snipe. Boulton & Paul's disappointment was slightly assuaged when they received orders to build 500 Snipes, though only 425 had been completed when orders were cancelled after the end of the War.

Also during the War Boulton & Paul built 7,835 propellers and the hulls of seventy Felixtowe F.3 and F.5 flying boats, produced them ten at a time in special revolving jigs. The next company design completed was the P.6 an experimental biplane designed to test various

John Dudley North, one of the great aviation pioneers and the guiding light of Boulton Paul Aircraft from 1917 to his death in 1968.

aerofoil sections, one of the first one-off experimental aircraft on the world, and designed to make further history after the War. Pressed into service as the company's own executive aircraft it made the first ever official business flight in this country. On the day the Air Navigation Act came into force on 1st April 1919, the Sales Manager flew in the P.6 to Bury St. Edmunds, completed a deal and flew home.

The other Boulton & Paul aircraft designed during the War, the P.7 Bourges, was destined to fix the company's direction for the next fifteen years. Originally designed as a twin-engined fighter-bomber it was in effect a fully aerobatic medium bomber of outstanding performance, but because of the delays with the Dragonfly engines for which it was designed it came just too late to secure the large orders it deserved and only three prototypes were built.

J.D. North's post-War strategy was three fold. An enlarged version of the P.6, the P.9 was produced to cater for a hoped-for boom in private flying, but struggled to compete with dirt-cheap, war surplus Avro 504s and only eight were built. Four were exported to Australia and one of these made the first aerial crossing of the Bass Strait from Tasmania to the mainland.

An airliner based on the Bourges was also produced, the P.8 Atlantic, the first being prepared for a bid to win the *Daily Mail* prize for the first non-stop transatlantic flight. Technically the best aircraft built for the flight, the first P.8 unfortunately crashed on its first take-off because of a fuel-flow problem, and Alcock and Brown's Vickers Vimy won all the plaudits and the *Daily Mail*'s £10,000. Though a second Atlantic was built and placed on the civil register, the very power of the two Napier Lion engines which made it the fastest twin-engined aircraft of its day, and enabled it to fly with one engine stopped, made it too expensive for the fragile airline economics of the time.

Finally J.D. North decided that the future of aviation lay in metal construction and adopted a comprehensive research programme which involved building an experimental two-seat biplane with an all steel structure, which caused something of a sensation at the 1919 Paris Air Show. Success for this strategy came with prototype orders for two twin-engined medium bombers with all-metal airframes a P.15 Bolton, and two experimental P.12 Bodmins, with the engines in their fuselage driving propellers through a series of shafts and gears.

A Boulton & Paul Sidestrands climbing away from Mousehold Airfield in 1926, with Boulton & Paul's Mousehold hangers below.

Boulton & Paul was able further to refine its knowledge of metal airframes, with a series of prototype orders totalling seven aircraft, for another twin-engined medium bomber, the P.25 Bugle. The company had become a specialist in the design of such high performance, aerobatic twin-engined medium bombers, but unfortunately the RAF felt this was one category of aircraft it could do without, preferring to order slow heavy night bombers and single engined 'medium' bombers with its limited resources.

Finally its persistence paid off in 1926 when two prototypes of a new twin-engined medium bomber were produced, the P.29 Sidestrand, named after a small Norfolk village where the Secretary of State for Air just happened to live! For the first time the company employed a full-time Test Pilot in Sqd. Ldr. C.A. Rea, who made the first flight of the Sidestrand. Previously most test flying had been done by a freelance test pilot, Frank Courtney, known widely in the Press as the Man with Magic Hands. The performance of the Sidestrand was such that the RAF decided to order eighteen Sidestrands to equip one squadron as an experiment. No.101 Squadron was reformed to fly them, and renewed its association with Boulton & Paul products having been equipped with FE.2Bs in the First World War.

Also that year Boulton & Paul were awarded the contract for the detail design and construction of the entire airframe of the R.101 Airship, which was assembled at the nationalised Royal Airship Works, Cardington. This huge contract, a recognition of the company's expertise in metal construction, was carried out in exemplory manner, and of the many contributing causes for the crash of the R.101, on its maiden flight to India, none could be laid at the door of Boulton & Paul.

Further evidence of official recognition of Boulton & Paul's skills in metal-working came when they were chosen to exploit the invention of the Townend Ring. Devised by H.C. Townend of the National Physics Laboratory the Ring was a close cowling for radial engines which greatly reduced their drag and increased performance.

Throughout the 1920s Boulton & Paul tried to break out of the mould of being considered

Five Boulton Paul Overstrands of No.101 Squadron. The last of the RAF biplane bombers they were the first aircraft in the World with a fully enclosed power-operated gun turret.

medium bomber specialists. They built two prototypes to one of the Government's bomber destroyer specifications, the P.31 Bitterns, the second of which continued North's association with moving guns by having Lewis guns in revolving barbettes on each side of the nose. They built both the heavy three-engined bomber, the P.32, and single-engine fighter, the P.33 Partridge, to official specifications, but manufacturers more normally associated with these areas of expertise won the RAF orders.

The company tried its hand in the light aircraft market once more producing the P.41 Phoenix with an ABC Scorpion engine. When this proved too small the aircraft was rebuilt as the Phoenix II with a more powerful Salmson radial, and a welded steel tube fuselage. There were no orders for the Phoenix, the De Havilland Moth having proven the optimum size for a light aircraft, but the company's development of welded structure lead to them building the wings for the Blackburn Bluebird and B.2.

Another one-off aircraft built was the P.64 Mailplane, a twin-engined aircraft designed to an Imperial Airways requirement for an aircraft capable of carrying 1,000 lbs of mail at 150 mph for 1,000 miles. The P.64 was the ultimate in twin-engined high performance biplane design, but Imperial Airways decided against a dedicated mail-carrier, and the sole P.64 crashed on trials at Martlesham Heath.

Boulton & Paul did receive an order for two Feederliner versions of the P.64, designed the P.71A, these 7/8 passenger aircraft had lower power than the P.64, but still retained a high performance for a biplane design. Despite high hopes that this small airliner programme would lead to further orders it was not to be, the age of the biplane was already passing.

The basis for the company's future was already taking shape however. In 1933 they were asked by the Air Ministry to consider ways of protecting the front gunner of the Sidestrand from the effect of the 140 mph slipstream, and eventually came up with a fully enclosed pneumatically-powered gun turret. This was fitted to one of the Sidestrands, together with other changes, including more powerful Pegasus engines replacing the Jupiters, a canopy for the pilot, and a larger windscreen for the dorsal gunner. Such were the changes to the aircraft that

Boulton Paul's factory at Pendeford in 1940, with Defiant on the apron to the left, next to the two T.2 hanger just being built. The roof of the new turret factory is being frantically camouflaged. Note the eight buses on the other side of the canal, unable to cross before the new bridge was built.

it was given a new project number and name, the P.75 Overstrand, named after another Norfolk village.

The gun turret was a huge success and three more Sidestrands were converted, and twenty four new Overstrands were ordered to re-equip No.101 Squadron, but these were destined to be the product of a new company.

Boulton & Paul had suffered through the Depression like most companies, and it was decided that the aircraft department was the weakest of the four divisions. Therefore in 1934 it was sold off to an investment group and became Boulton Paul Aircraft Ltd, continuing in the same premises at Mousehold for a time, now rented from its former parent, but looking for a site for a new factory.

At the time the town of Wolverhampton was planning a new Municipal Airport at Barnhurst Farm, Pendeford, and offered Boulton Paul a site near its boundary and flying rights for a 100 years. With an abundant supply of skilled engineering workers in Wolverhampton and the Black Country, the company chose to move to Wolverhampton, and construction of the new factory began in 1935, with steelwork from its former parent, Boulton & Paul Ltd.

In hindsight it can be seen that the aircraft division was sold off just as the good times were going to start. With the build up of the RAF which gathered pace in the late 30s orders began to flood in. The Overstrand was the last complete aircraft built at Norwich, but several new contracts were initiated there only to be completed at Wolverhampton. There were spars for Blackburn Sharks, the complete wings for the Saro London flying boat, Fairey Seafox tails, and orders totalling 106 No for the Hawker Demon.

All of the Demons first flew from Wolverhampton, and many of them were fitted with the new Frazer-Nash FN.1 'Lobsterback' gun turret, making them the first of the 'turret fighters' the aircraft with which Boulton Paul was suddenly associated.

The construction of the prototypes of their own turret fighter, the P.82 Defiant, had begun in Norwich, but was completed in Wolverhampton, first flying in August 1937, though at first

Six Defiants of No 264 (Madras Presidency) Squadron early in 1940, the first and most successful Defiant squadrons.

without the turret for which it was designed. The four-gun Defiant turret was basically a French design, The SAMM AB.7 designed by Antoine de Boysson. It as an electro-hydraulic design, with its own hydraulic motor, and self contained except for electrical power from the parent aircraft. The French Government had not been interested in the turret, and so SAMM offered it to Boulton Paul, knowing of their Overstrand turret. J.D. North went to France to see it, and recognised immediately that it was superior to his own pneumatic design. He bought the rights to it, and set the new course for the company which has lasted to the present day.

The whole of the company completed the move to Wolverhampton during 1936, most of the 600 strong workforce choosing to go, though not Sqd. Ldr. Rea who started his own company in the vacated buildings at Mousehold. The new Chief Test Pilot was Fl. Lt. Cecil Feather, and it was he who made the first flight of the new Defiant. Boulton Paul, from being renowned as a manufacturer of twin-engined biplane medium bombers, now suddenly found itself working on four of the new turret fighters.

The Hawker Demon was being built in the factory alongside the prototypes of two new designs, Boulton Paul's own Defiant, and the Blackburn Roc. Blackburn had won the contest to find a new naval turret fighter with a version of their Skua fitted with one of the new Boulton Paul four-gun turrets, but their design department was overstretched both with the Skua and the forthcoming Botha, and so Boulton Paul took over the detail design of the new Roc, and all Rocs were built at Pendeford.

Yet while these three turret fighters were in production, or being readied for production, the Defiant's replacement, the P.92, a twin-engined design with a four-cannon turret was already being worked on, and orders were placed for three prototypes, but though started the P.92 was eventually cancelled.

By the beginning of the War both the Roc and the Defiant were in full production. The factory had already been increased in size by eighty per cent, and a new turret factory extension

The front of the Dowty Boulton Paul factory in 1980. The words 'Boulton Paul' have gone now, apart from a small plaque by the front door.

was planned to cope with the huge orders which were flooding in for the whole range of Boulton Paul turrets. Apart from the Type A dorsal turret for the Defiant and Roc, there were the Type C nose turret, Type E tail turret and Type K ventral turret for the new Halifax heavy bomber, and the new Type A and Type K for the Albermarle.

Being self contained, unlike Frazer Nash turrets which required hydraulic lines to the parent aircraft, Boulton Paul turrets were chosen for fitment to the American aircraft which were being purchased, the Lockhead Hudson, and then the Baltimore, Liberator and Ventura. Turret production was eventually handed over to Joseph Lucas leaving Boulton Paul to concentrate on turret development and aircraft production.

The Defiant went into service with No.264 Squadron, who developed tactics which enabled the aircraft to at least hold its own when attacked by Bf. 109s. On 29th May 1940, over the beaches of Dunkirk No. 264 Squadron's Defiants claimed thirty seven German aircraft shot down for no loss to themselves, which still stands as a record. Over Dunkirk and in the Battle of Britain the Defiants continued to shoot down three Germans for every Defiant lost, but with the Luftwaffe turning to night operations in the autumn of 1940, the Defiant was the best night-fighter available, faster than the Blenheim and more effective than single-seaters, and so the Defiant Squadrons were moved to night operation.

Boulton Paul produced 1,062 Defiants in all, and then the Fairey Barracuda took over the production lines, 692 of these being built before contracts were cancelled at the end of the War. Post War the factory was filled with Wellington bombers, 270 of them being completely stripped, overhauled and converted to navigation trainers.

At the same time the RAF's new advanced trainer was taking shape, the P.108 Balliol. Envisaged as a turboprop aircraft, only three Mamba-powered Balliol T.1s were built before the decision was made to power production Balliols with war surplus Merlin engines. A further change of mind meant only 226 Balliol T.2s and Sea Balliols for the Fleet Air Arm were built in all, and Vampire T.11 became the RAF's advanced trainers.

Two more aircraft of Boulton Paul's own design were built, the P.111 and P.120 experimental delta wing jets, but these were equipped with early versions of Boulton Paul power control units, and it was in the production of PCUs that the future of the company now lay.

The electro-hydraulic technology of the gun turrets had naturally lead to the design and production of PCUs which were fitted to a number of aircraft, the Valiant, Vulcan, Buccaneer, VC-10, and BAC.111. In an era of aircraft company mergers, J.D. North, now Chairman, sought to merge with the company started by his old friend, George Dowty, and the Pendeford company because Dowty Boulton Paul Ltd, in a strengthened Dowty Group.

The company continued to lead the World in PCU development, and in particular Fly-by-Wire. They had already flown the first aircraft in the World with electric signalling on all three axes, the Tay-Viscount, and were soon to win the most prestigious of all contracts, supplying PCUs for Concorde.

In 1968 J.D. North died, after 51 years at the helm of the company. He was perhaps the most unsung of all the great British aviation pioneers. The innovation and invention which has always been a tenet of Boulton Paul's philosophy was a product of his making. He always tried to keep the company one step ahead of its competitors, and it is this reason more than any other which kept the company in existence when so many more illustrious names have fallen by the wayside.

It still produces high technology aerospace products, not only fly-by-wire systems and PCUs but also propellant tanks and valves for spacecraft. In 1991 the company began trading as Dowty Aerospace Wolverhampton, with a sister company within the Dowty Group in California. It was the disappearance of the name Boulton Paul from in front of the factory, apart from the small company nameplate, which prompted the formation of the Boulton Paul Association, to preserve the long history of the company, in all its guises.

One

Boulton & Paul Ltd

The old established Norwich company of Boulton & Paul Ltd began making aeroplanes in 1915, firstly at its Riverside Works and later at Mousehold Airport. They created their own design department in 1917 with J.D. North as Chief Engineer.

In all they built 2,628 aircraft in Norwich, though only seventy eight of their own design, and strictly speaking twenty six of these were after Boulton & Paul had sold off its aircraft division in 1934.

They were most closely associated with the production of high performance, fully aerobatic twin-engined medium bombers, epitomised by the Sidestrand and Overstrand, but were also well known for being pioneers in metal aircraft construction. Their biggest single contract was the design and construction of the entire airframe of the biggest 'aircraft' ever built in this country, the R.101 airship.

The first Bugle. J6984, at Mousehold, in 1923. The Bugle was one of a series of high-performance twin-engined biplane medium bombers built by the company in Norwich. The man at the top of the right hand ladder is Bill Monument who was one of the 600 workers who later moved with the company to Wolverhampton.

The first aircraft built by Boulton & Paul was the FE.2B, powered by the 160 hp Beardmore, 250 No being completed from October 1915. They were followed by 300 No. FE.2Ds with the Rolls-Royce Eagle, including this one A6389.

A Sopwith Camel, B9280, at Mousehold, one of 1,575 Camels built by Boulton & Paul, making them equal with Ruston Proctor as the largest manufacturers of Camel, and they averaged twenty eight per week over the duration of production.

The sole surviving aircraft built by Boulton & Paul at Norwich is this Camel, F6314, pictured here on Horse Guards Parade, and now in the RAF museum at Hendon.

In late June 1917 the company decided to create its own Aircraft Design Department and recruited John Dudley North to become Chief Engineer. He had this post before the War at Grahame-White Aviation, and designed this aircraft amongst others, the Type 10 Charabanc, which set a World Record by lifting ten people aloft. J.D. North is in the bow-tie, and Cluade Grahame-White is in front in the pilot's seat.

Boulton & Paul built hulls of seventy Felixtowe F.3 and F.5 flying boats, their woodworking skills being ideal for the job, as can be seen from this photograph of one of them under construction.

The first Boulton & Paul design to be completed was the P.3 Bobolink, C8655, and named after a North American bird. It is pictured in December 1917 having been erected at Riverside Works. The Bentley BR.2 engine is without its cowling.

The Bobolink had two Vickers machine guns and could take a moveable Lewis gun on a sliding rail, shown here pointing directly upwards. The covers over the fuel tanks, behind the cockpit are not yet fitted.

Shown fully erected at Mousehold, the Bobolink was intended to be a Sopwith Camel replacement, and was in competition with a number of other designs.

The sole Bobolink at Martlesham Heath in March 1918, where it lost out on competition with the Sopwith Snipe, and the second two prototypes were cancelled before being built.

The Bobolink back at Mousehold in June 1918, with a horn balance fitted to the front rudder. Its final fate has not been recorded.

CORNER OF SEWING ROOM.

COVERING THE PLANES.

AN END OF VARNISH SHOP.

VIEW OF DOPING ROOM.

Four views of wings and control surfaces being covered and doped. As can be seen most of the wartime workforce in these departments was female.

Boulton & Paul received orders for 500 Sopwith Snipes, as seen here at Mousehold, but only 425 had been delivered when orders were cancelled in 1919.

The Boulton & Paul P.6, built specifically to test various aerofoil sections, but put in use after the War as a company transport. The serial X-25 is from a specific range devoted to such experimental aircraft. There is a Snipe in the hanger behind.

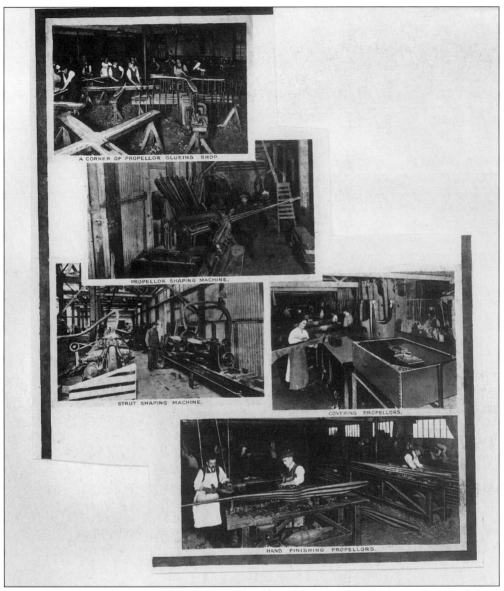

A CORNER OF PROPELLOR GLUEING SHOP.

PROPELLOR SHAPING MACHINE.

STRUT SHAPING MACHINE.

COVERING PROPELLORS.

HAND FINISHING PROPELLORS.

During the War Boulton & Paul used its woodworking skills to make 7,835 propellers, and these photographs show some of the shops engaged in the difficult processes.

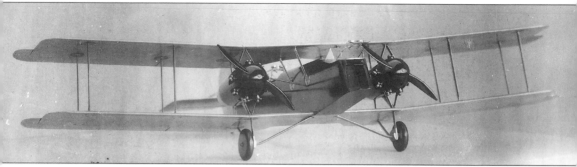

This is a fine 1918 model of the P.7 Bourges, a fighter-bomber powered by two 300 hp ABC
Dragonfly engines, three prototypes of which where ordered. It was named after a French town.
(As were the Vickers Vimy and the DH.10 Amiens).

The Boulton & Paul P.6 outside a hanger in the rain. It can also be seen that the company
name and 'Sales Dept.' has also been applied to the lower wing. The engine was a 90 hp
RAF.1A air-cooled V-8.

On the 1st April 1919 the P.6 had the honour of making the first official business flight in this country. On the day the new Air Aviation Act came into force the Sales Manager flew to Bury St. Edmunds, completed a deal, and flew home.

The first prototype P.7 Bourges, F2903, fitted for its early flights with 230 hp Bentley BR.2 rotary engines because the Dragonfly radials were not yet ready.

A rare shot of Bourges F2903 from the ground, and before horn balanced ailerons were fitted. The aircraft had an outstanding performance even with the lower powered engines.

Bourges F2903 with the Dragonfly radials now fitted. These engines suffered appalling overheating and vibration problems. the nose-gunners position can be seen, with its bomb-aiming window, and the pilot's cockpit just behind. There was also a dorsal gunner.

The Bourges was the first twin-engined aircraft which was fully-aerobatic and could be looped, rolled and spun. It is seen here upside down over the Norfolk countryside.

The second Bourges, F2904 had a radically different configuration. The Dragonfly engines were sited on the lower wing rather than at mid-gap, and the upper wing was gulled to give the crew a better all-round view.

Bourges F2904 crashed at Mousehold during 1919, but this was not the end of the aircraft as the remains were used to build one of the P.8 Atlantics.

The third Bourges, F2905, dispensed with the awful Dragonfly radials and had two 450 hp water-cooled Napier Lions, mounted on the lower wing, but with the wing configuration of the first prototype.

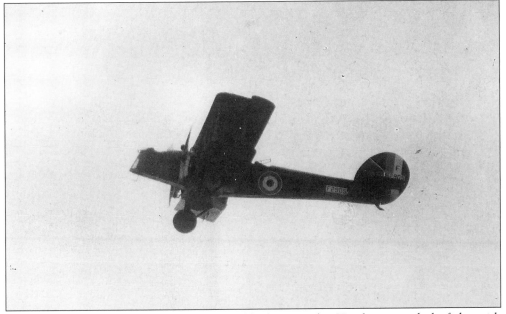

A rare air to air shot of F2905, which appeared had appeared at Hendon in mock-dogfights with RAF fighters as late as 1923. The Bourges was a marvellous aircraft produced just too late for the War, but it set the company on the course it would follow, building superlative twin-engined medium bombers.

DRILLING MACHINES.

AUTOMATIC & CAPSTAN LATHES.

ACETYLENE WELDERS.

R.A.F. WIRE ASSEMBLING.

PRESS DEPARTMENT.

Although known mostly as woodworkers, Boulton & Paul were noted metal-workers too, and produced every part of the aircraft they built except the engines and armament. As can be seen by these photographs the wartime workers were largely female.

Boulton & Paul's post-War strategy including production of airliner versions of the Bourges, and to publicise it planned to win the *Daily Mail*'s £10,000 prize for the first non-stop Atlantic crossing. The P.8 Atlantic is shown at Mousehold early in 1919.

This is a contemporary artist's impression of the P.8 Atlantic in flight. As can be seen the pilot had a fully enclosed cockpit, and the navigator and wireless operator sat in an enclosed cabin.

This is a close-up of one of the Atlantic's 450 hp Napier Lion engines which made it the fastest twin-engined aircraft of its day, and on the transatlantic flight would have meant it could maintain altitude on one engine after two hour's flight had been used up.

The navigator for the transatlantic flight was to be J.H. Wollner (left), seen in April 1919, talking to Frank Courtney who was Boulton & Paul's test pilot until 1925, on a freelance basis.

The first flight of the P.8 Atlantic ended in this crash when one engine cut on take-off, caused by Frank Courtney having been hurried in his pre-flight preparations by dignitaries who had a train to catch!

The Atlantic was envisaged as a 7-8 passenger airliner as seen in this artist's impression, with two cabins fore and aft of the wing. As can be seen an open cockpit was also offered, to assuage the prejudices of contemporary pilots.

A second Atlantic was built and registered G-EAPE, but there were no airline orders. The very power which gave it single-engined safety, made it uneconomic for the infant airlines of the day.

The second stand of the company's post-War strategy was a slightly enlarged version of the wartime P.6, the P.9, powered by the same RAF.1A engine. The first, shown under construction in May 1919, was to the order of Lt. Long.

Long's P.9 at Mousehold on completion, after which he took it to Australia. Subsequent P.9s differed in detail from Long's aircraft.

Lt. Long used his P.9 to make the first flight from Tasmania to the mainland across the Bass Strait, as shown in these photographs. He had already made the first newspaper delivery flight in Australia, in his P.9.

This is P.9, G-EAPD, one of seven subsequent production aircraft. They had altered centre-section struts and built-in suitcases behind the rear cockpits.

(1) HEAT TREATMENT ROOM.
(2) SHEET METAL SHOP.
(3) FITTER'S SHOP.

(1)

(2)

(3)

(4)

(5)

(6)

)OM.
G DEPARTMENT.
& ALUMINIUM FOUNDRY.

The final part of the company's post-War strategy was a move into metal aircraft construction. As can be seen from these pictures of various wartime departments they already had an extensive expertise in metal.

This is the fuselage of the P.10s under construction, the company's first attempt at an all-metal airframe. The fuselage panels are Bakelite-Dilecto, probably the first application of plastic in an aircraft's structure.

Another view of the P.10s fuselage, showing the firewall. Apart from the strip-steel structure it was conventional-looking two-seater biplane.

The P.10 on display at the 1919 Paris Air Show. It was the sensation of the Show, but there is no evidence that it was ever completed and flown. Like the 'concept cars' often displayed at the Motor Show it had proven the techniques, but was not intended for production.

The starboard lower wing of the P.10 on display at the Aerospace Museum, Cosford in 1993. The oldest British metal aircraft wing in existence it had been borrowed by the Boulton Paul Association from the Bridewell Museum, Norwich, which also owns the P.10 fin and rudder.

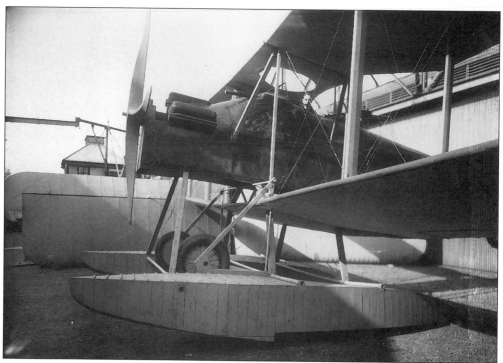

An impressive mock-up of the Boulton & Paul P.11 at Riverside in 1919. It was aimed at RAF Specification Types XXI, for an amphibian. In the background can be seen a Bourges or Atlantic upper wing.

A front view of the mock-up showing the wheels down and the larger propeller of the Napier Lion engine.

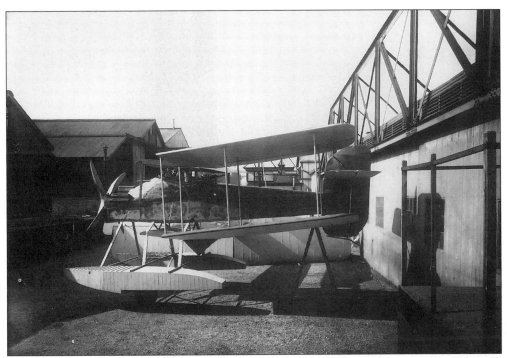

Part of Specification Type XXI called for folding wings. The closeness of the pilot and gunner's cockpit can also be seen in this view.

A front view of P.11, which was not ordered. Three prototypes of the rival Fairey Pintail were ordered, followed by three production Pintails for Japan.

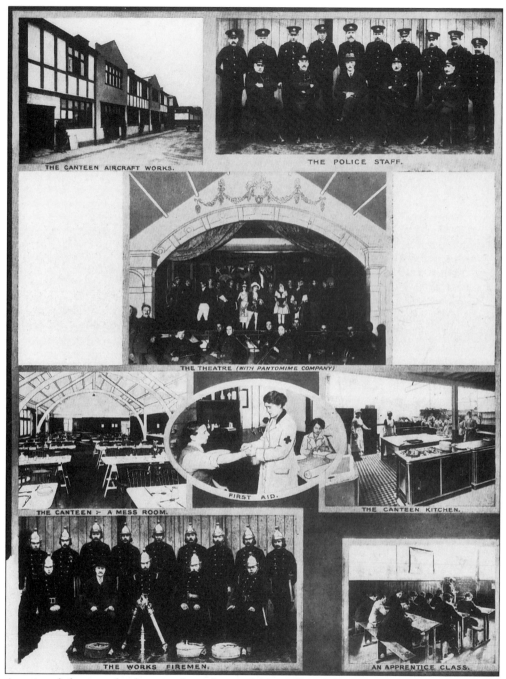

THE CANTEEN AIRCRAFT WORKS.

THE POLICE STAFF.

THE THEATRE (WITH PANTOMIME COMPANY)

THE CANTEEN :- A MESS ROOM.

FIRST AID.

THE CANTEEN KITCHEN.

THE WORKS FIREMEN.

AN APPRENTICE CLASS.

A series of photographs showing the police and fire staff, and the company's canteen facilities first-aid treatment, apprentice classroom and theatre.

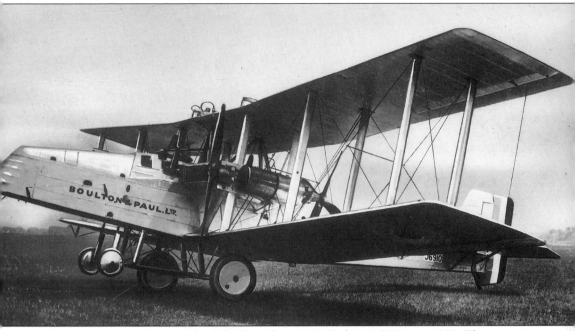

A slightly retouched photograph of the first of two P.12 Bodmins, J6910, in 1923. This was an experimental layout for a bomber with the two Napier Lion engines in the fuselage driving pusher and tractor propellers through a series of shafts and gears.

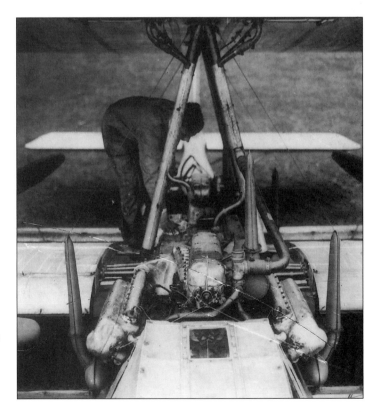

The 'engine room' of the P.12 Bodmin. The mechanic could work on the engines in flight inside the fuselage. The extra weight of the shafts and gears was more than made up the lighter steel structure, compared to a wooden airframe.

The Bodmin in front of one of the production P.9s, G-EBEQ, which was being prepared for the 1923 Aerial Derby at the time.

A rare picture of the P.12 Bodmin in the air, again the first prototype, J6910. No pictures of the second Bodmin, seem to exist.

Th P.15 Bolton medium bomber showing off its all-steel airframe. One prototype of a 'metal Bourges' was ordered, J6584, though the Bolton displayed little similarity to the Bourges, other than the general layout.

A side view of the Bolton in 1922. With the Bodmin also under construction at the time, Boulton & Paul were one of the major pioneers of metal construction, along with Short Bros. and Vickers.

The Bolton now covered and ready for delivery. This view shows the narrow-track undercarriage with the unusual nosewheel.

The Bolton was the first aircraft with an all-metal airframe ever delivered to the Royal Air Force, and was to continue the company's association with high performance medium bombers.

1919 ——— 1924

THE illustration above shows the first All-Metal Aeroplane exhibited by Boulton & Paul Ltd., at the Paris Exhibition in 1919, and demonstrates that five years ago the broad outline of the Boulton & Paul system of metal construction had taken form. Since that time, Boulton & Paul Ltd. have been continuously engaged in the design and construction of Metal Aeroplanes on an extensive scale. Their unique experience ensures proved reliable Aeroplanes.

THIS advertisement is the first of an interesting series of announcements dealing with the design and construction of Boulton & Paul Aeroplanes, to appear at regular intervals in this journal.

Boulton & Paul Ltd

Telegrams
BOULTON NORWICH **NORWICH** NORWICH 851 (5 lines) Telephone

LONDON OFFICE 135-137 QUEEN VICTORIA ST. E.C
Telegrams Boutique Cent London Telephone 4642 Cent

Contractors to The Air Ministry, The Admiralty, The War Office, H.M. Board of Works, The Crown Agent for the Colonies, English, South American and Indian Railways, Soudan, South African and Egyptian Governments.

One of a series of company advertisements in the 1920s which emphasised their pioneering work in metal structures.

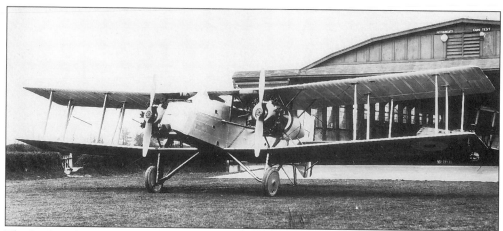

The P.25 Bugle prototype J6984 at Mousehold. Frank Courtney made its first flight on 24th July 1923. It was the next stage in Boulton & Paul's development of the medium bomber, and much more like the Bourges than its predecessor, the Bolton. A P.12 Bodmin is in the hanger behind.

A rear view of the second Bugle, J6985. Five Bristol Jupiter-powered prototypes were built, orders which enabled the company to keep ticking over. The RAF had no place for twin-engined medium bombers in its inventory.

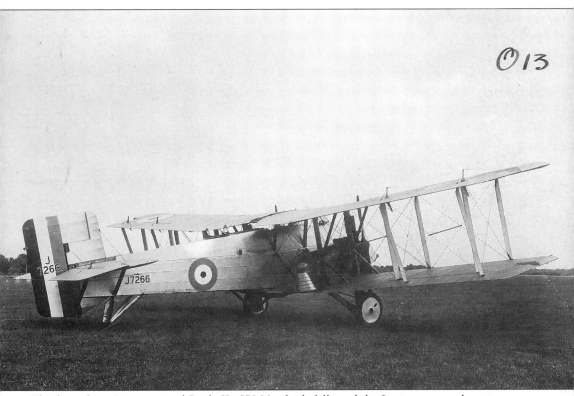

The first of two Lion-engined Bugle IIs, J7266, which followed the Jupiter-powered versions.

A front view of the Bugle IIs, showing the stepped down position of the nose gunner, and the wide-track of the undercarriage.

Boulton & Paul's expertise in metal structures lead to them being given the order by the Royal Airships Works for the detail design and manufacture of the complete structure of the R.101 airship. This is some of the machinery engaged on that structure.

This is one of the 70 ft. long transverse girders of the R.101 under construction at Norwich. All the parts of the structure were transported to Cardington for assembly.

An internal photograph of the R.101 under construction showing the central walkway which ran through the hull.

The R.101 Airship at Cardington, the largest 'aircraft' ever built in this country it suffered from serious design flaws, none of them attributable to Boulton & Paul's structure.

The R.101 in the air over Norfolk. It crashed on its maiden flight to India, and put paid to the British Aircraft Programme, much to the disappointment of Boulton & Paul who expected more work on airships.

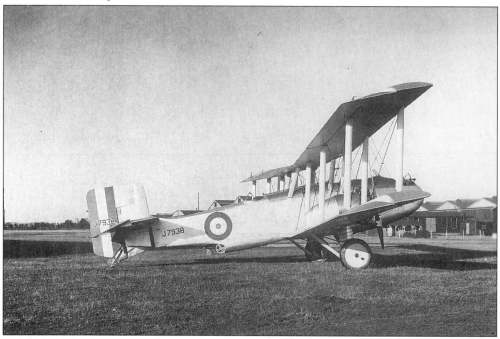

The prototype of the P.29 Sidestrand, named after a small Norfolk village, at Mousehold in 1926. The first flight was made by Boulton & Paul's new permanent Chief Test Pilot, Sqd. Ldr. C.A. Rea.

An internal shot of the Sidestrand's structure. The company's steel structures had been refined to a considerable degree by now.

The Sidestrand's wing showing the rear spar. Boulton & Paul were offering a catalogue of standard metal components, and a number of other companies used their expertise.

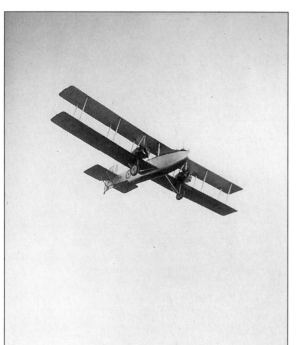

The Sidestrand on its first flight over Mousehold, showing the company's distinctive square-cut wings and tail.

A head-on view of the Sidestrand prototype showing the slim lines of the fuselage, and the low-wing position of the Jupiter engines. The RAF finally decided to order twin engined medium bombers as an experiment, and eighteen production Sidestrands followed the prototypes to equip one squadron.

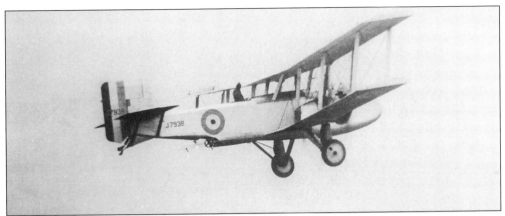

The Sidestrand prototype climbing away from Mousehold. The ventral, prone gun position can be seen. It or the dorsal position, was to be manned by the rear gunner according to the aircraft's position in a formation.

Three Sidestrands of No.101 Squadron in formation. The upper and lower surfaces of the fuselage and the nacelles were painted green to prevent glare.

The nose of the Sidestrand could be folded thus to gain access to the front gunner's position. Note the tip-up seat on the port side.

A Sidestrand's Jupiter engine cowled with a Townend Ring, which reduced drag. Boulton & Paul were chosen to exploit this invention, which had been devised by Dr H.C. Townend of the National Physics Laboratory.

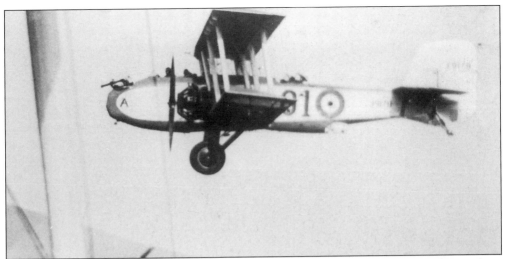

An air to air shot of a No.101 Squadron Sidestrand III, J9178. Note a figure in the auxiliary second crew position behind the pilot.

Five No.101 Squadron Sidestrands against a cloudscape. The steadiness of the aircraft enabled the Squadron to win the RAF's annual bombing trophy.

A close-up of one of the Sidestrand's Jupiter engines which gave it high top speed of 140mph making life difficult for the nose gunners trying to train his Lewis gun against the slipstream.

This is the second prototype Sidestrand, J7939, which was used by the company for trials of various modifications, and shown here with Pegasus engines, with four-blade propellers, and the Sidestrand III's revised bomb-aiming window.

No.101 Squadron's Sidestrands at dispersal at Andover.

A group of the company's luminaries at Mousehold in 1933. Left to right: Major Jack Stewart, Capt. J. Dawson Paul (Chairman), John Carter, J.D. North (Chief Engineer) and Sqd. Ldr. C.A. Rea (Test Pilot).

The first of two prototypes of the P.31 Bittern, J7936. A single-seat twin-engined monoplane fighter it was far ahead of its time. The second Bittern, J7937 had two Lewis guns in revolving barbettes on each side of the nose, to enable the fire upwards.

A rear view of the Bittern at Mousehold. It had two 230 hp Lynx engines. Entry to the cockpit was via two steps which can be seen in the fuselage side, and then along the top of the fuselage.

The largest aircraft Boulton & Paul ever built was the sole P.32 heavy bomber, J9950, powered by three Bristol Jupiter radials, and armed with nose, dorsal and tail gun positions.

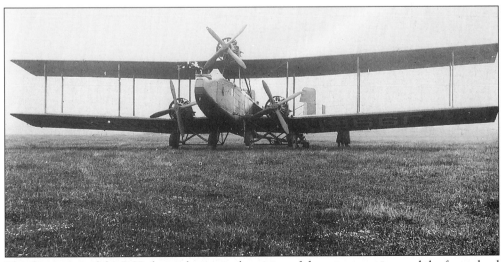

This front view of the P.32 shows the unusual position of the centre engine, and the four-wheel main undercarriage. The RAF decided to stick to twin-engined heavy bombers for the time being.

The P.32 appeared at the RAF Pageant at Hendon, carrying the New Types No.11 on the nose.

The P.33 Partridge fighter was aimed at Spec. F.9/26 to replace the RAF's Siskins and Gamecocks. The sole prototypes serial J8459, was one of nine designs competing for the order, which was won by the Bristol Bulldog.

The Partridge was powered by a Bristol Jupiter radial and the troughs for the two Vickers guns can be seen in the fuselage side.

A side view of the Partridge, showing in the shape of the fin and rudder and the square cut of the wings a family resemblance to the Sidestrand with which it shared a number of Boulton & Paul's standard components.

A rival to the Partridge, the Vickers Type 141 being refuelled at Mousehold during the 1929 King's Cup Air Race. J.D. North on the right, one of the officials for the race, is facing the pilot 'Mutt' Summers.

Boulton & Paul's last venture into the light aircraft market, the Phoenix II, G-AAIT. This two-seat monoplane had a welded tube metal fuselage and a Salmson radial replacing an earlier ABC Scorpion. No sales of the Phoenix were made and the prototype was used as a runabout by the company until 1935.

A side view of the Phoenix II. The large rudder was interchangeable with the elevators.

The Jupiter-powered P.64 Mailplane in the air. It was designed to an Imperial Airways requirement for an aircraft capable of carrying 1,000 lbs of mail at 150 mph for 1,000 miles at half power. It was the epitome of high performance biplane design, faster than contemporary RAF fighters.

65

Only one P.64 was built, G-ABYK, as Imperial Airways decided against a dedicated mailplane. It is shown here displaying its clean lines flying over Norwich.

Another air-to-air shot of the P.64 showing the nine-sided Townend Rings which closely cowled the engines.

The P.64 landing at Mousehold. The first flight of the P.64 ended with disaster when on landing, Sqd. Ldr. Rea ran over a cricket pitch and the fence surrounding the square tipped the aircraft on its nose.

The P.64 with small extra fins added to the tailplane to cure a slight directional instability. The aircraft crashed at Martlesham Heath while under test.

The P.64 lead to the P.71A Feederliner, two of which were ordered by Imperial Airways, this being the first G-ACOX. They could carry 7/8 passengers at high cruising speed, despite having lower power than the P.64.

The second view of the P.71A, G-ACOY in the air. Unfortunately both of these aircraft crashed while in Imperial Airways Service.

A front view of the P.71A Feederliner showing the clean lines.

The mock-up of the company's solution to the problems of the Sidestrand's nose gunner, a fully-enclosed, power-operated gun turret. One of the armament staff sits in the bomb-aiming position, with the Lewis gun stowed.

A converted Sidestrand III with the new gun turret in the nose, a fully enclosed canopy for the pilot, and a large screen for the dorsal gunner. With more powerful Pegasus engines, and other changes, the aircraft was given a new name, the P.75 Overstrand, named after another Norfolk village.

The Overstrand prototype, showing its pneumatically-operated gun turret which increased the efficiency of the nose gunner from 15% to 85%. Three more Overstrands were converted and 24 new Overstrands were ordered to re-equip and enlarge No.101 Squadron.

A close-up of the nine-sided Townend Ring fitted to the Overstrand's Bristol Pegasus radials. The Overstrand had a top speed of 153 mph.

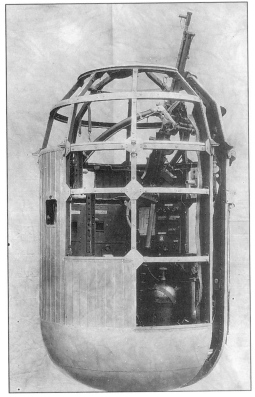

The Overstrand's turret showing the gun in the stowed position. The vertical slot could be closed by zip fastener. The turret could revolve through 360 degrees with the gun in this position.

A No.101 Squadron Overstrand, J9179, in front of one of the Sidestrands it was replacing, at Bicester.

A mock-up of a twin Lewis gun pneumatic tail turret for the P.79 project to Spec. B.3/34, the one which produced the Hampden and Wellington.

Overstrand, K4556, after an accident at Bicester caused by a Flight Commander landing on boggy ground.

One of the last things ever built at Mousehold, the mock-up of a tail turret for the P.90 four-engined heavy bomber project, with twin guns on articulating pods.

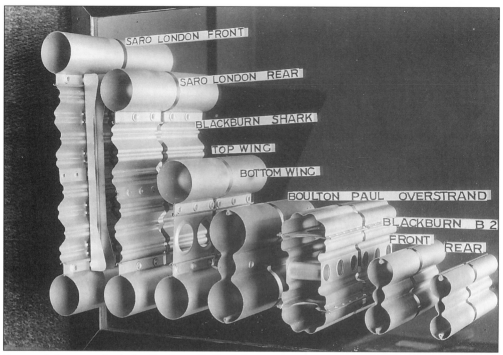

Some of the spars built by Boulton & Paul for various companies. They built the complete wings for the Saro London flying boat and the Blackburn B-2 and Bluebird IV light aircraft.

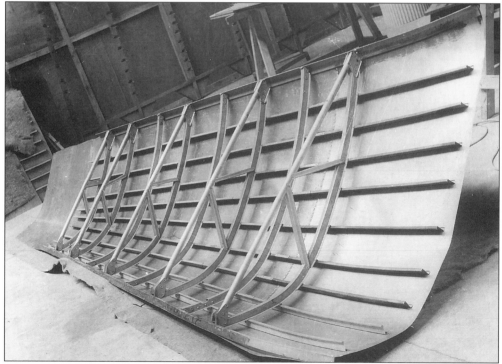

A glimpse of the future. One rear fuselage side of the Defiant prototype at Mousehold in 1936, shortly before the company moved to Wolverhampton, where the aircraft was assembled.

Two
Boulton Paul
Aircraft Ltd

After being sold off in 1934 the newly independent company, Boulton Paul Aircraft Ltd moved to a brand new factory at Pendeford Airport, Wolverhampton in 1936. Here they quickly became known as manufacturers of turret fighters, the Hawker Demon, the Blackburn Roc and their own Defiant, the most famous aircraft ever produced by Boulton Paul.

They built 2,198 aircraft at Wolverhampton, including 1,263 of their own design, and were also well known for their electro-hydraulic gun turrets, which had many applications. Their last production aircraft was the Balliol advanced trainer, the last being delivered in 1955.

The most important aircraft in their history however, in terms of volume of work, and years of association, was the Canberra, Boulton Paul performing a host of modification work at Pendeford and its Flight Test Centre at Seighford.

The company's most important new product as the Fifties progressed became the power-assisted controls for which it is now world famous.

Company test pilot Robin Lindsay Neale climbing aboard a Blackburn Roc turret fighter outside the new factory of Boulton Paul Aircraft at Pendeford, Wolverhampton.

The offices of the new factory under construction in 1936. Originally single storey they faced the Wobaston Road, with the factory behind them leading to the taxiway to the new Wolverhampton Municipal Airport. They were later made two-storey.

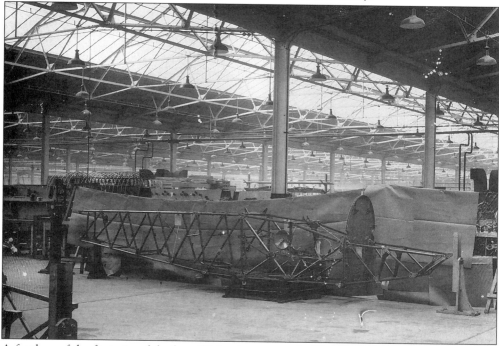

A fuselage of the first aircraft built at Wolverhampton, the Hawker Demon two-seater fighter. The company built a total of 106 Demons.

A Hawker Demon in the air. Some of the Boulton Paul built Demons had the Frazer-Nash FN.1 'Lobsterback' turret, though not this one.

The remains of the Boulton Paul-built Hawker Demon, K8203, seen in 1991, and now being rebuilt to fly, registered G-BTVE by Skysport Engineering for Aero Vintage.

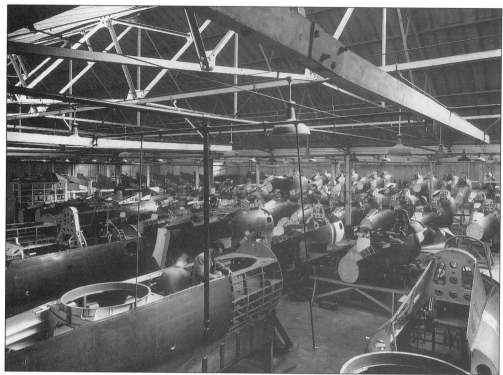

Blackburn Rocs in production in 1939. Boulton Paul did the detailed redesign of the Blackburn Skua to take their own four-gun Type A turret, and build all 136 Rocs.

Production Rocs outside the Flight Sheds in the winter of 1939. The factory had been camouflaged by then.

A production Roc, L3084 on flight test. The turret was basically the same as that in the Defiant, only the interrupter gear (preventing the gunner shooting off parts of his own aircraft) differed.

Three Rocs in service with the Fleet Air Arm. Never more than useless as fighters, being far too slow, they were soon relegated to second line duties such as target towing.

The prototype P.82 Defiant, K8310, in the form it made its first flight from Pendeford in 11th August 1937, at the hands of the new Chief Test Pilot Flt. Lt. Cecil Feather. It was not yet fitted with a turret. It is shown on the taxiway which ran from the factory to the airfield.

The prototype Defiant just after the turret was fitted for the first time. The Type A turret was based on the French SAMM AB.7 electro-hydraulic turret for which Boulton Paul had bought the rights.

The prototype with its turret outside the factory. The retractable fairings fore and aft of the turret are in their raised streamlined positions. They lowered as the guns passed over them.

The second prototype Defiant, K8320, early in 1939, before the factory was camouflaged. A production Roc is in the background. This was closer to production aircraft with stub exhausts, one piece windscreen, and other changes.

The Boulton Paul two-gun Type C turret being assembled. This was designed as a nose turret and used as such in the Halifax, but was also fitted as a dorsal turret in the Halifax, Hudson and early Ventura.

The Boulton Paul Company football team in the 1939-40 season.

An aerial view of the factory in 1940 showing the new gun-turret factory under construction, with the roof not yet camouflaged, and two Bellman hangers being erected by the apron as extra flight sheds. The village of Bilbrook is in the background and Pendeford Mill pool on the right.

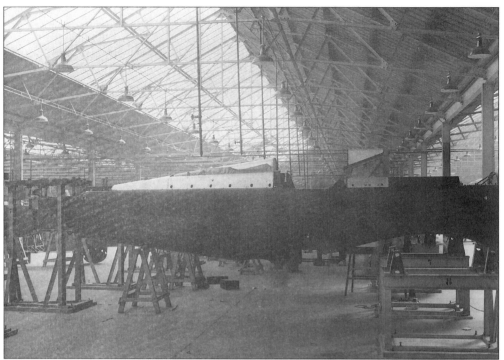

A Defiant fuselage under construction in 1940. As can be seen this sat on top of the centre wing section. The upper surface of the wing actually formed the pilot's cockpit floor.

Production Defiants lined up outside the factory in 1940. There were a total of 1,060 production Defiants following the two prototypes.

A production Defiant, N1650, being flight tested by Cecil Feather in July 1940. This aircraft went to No.256 Squadron, then No.7 Air Gunners School and was struck off charge in April 1943 with 144.30 flying hours.

129 The Defiant was fitted with racks to carry 8 x 20 lb. bombs for Army co-operation duties, but though tested by No.2 Squadron, it was never used in this role.

As in the first War hundreds of women were employed in the factory during the Second World War, and these two are making bulkhead formers for the Defiant gunner's cockpit.

As the Boulton Paul factory was isolated from the town of Wolverhampton, and an easy target, this dummy factory was built a mile further along the Shropshire Union canal (shown here still being built).

A self-contained Type A turret trainer, with its own generator to provide power for ground firing.

A production Defiant on a test flight as a German bomber would see it in a cross-over attack.

'A' flight of No.264 Squadron the first Defiant unit, which had conspicuous success over Dunkirk and in the Battle of Britain.

As they were self-contained, needing only an electrical supply, Boulton Paul turrets could be slotted into many applications. This one has been fitted for anti-aircraft defence on a patrol boat.

The electrically-retracted Type K ventral turret. Ordered in large numbers as the K. Mk.I for the Halifax and K.Mk.II for the Albermarle, the K.Mk.I was cancelled before completion and only one of the seventy K.Mk.IIs completed was ever fitted to an Albermarle.

The Duke of Kent alighting from the King's Flight Lockheed Hudson, showing the Boulton Paul Type C turret. It's domed shape was because its gun could be depressed 30 degrees and sufficient head room for the gunner was therefore required.

A Lockheed Hudson, N7251, at the factory in 1939 to have its Type C turret fitted. Most Hudson turrets were fitted elsewhere. Note the two men on the roof camouflaging the factory.

Robin Lindsay Neale about to test fly a
Defiant. After the War he succeeded
Cecil Feather as Chief Test Pilot.

A flight of No.264 Squadron. There were three different roundel types in evidence. The nearest
aircraft coded 'PS A' is Squadron Leader Phillip Hunter's. He devised tactics for the Defiant
which allows it to at least hold its own against Bf. 109s.

During the Battle of Britain the company offered several single-seat versions of the Defiant, and painted the prototype as shown. As a single seater the Defiant offered greater potential than the Hurricane, particularly as a naval fighter, but nothing was done.

Two old adversaries from Dunkirk at RAF St Athan in 1960. The RAF Museum's Defiant, N1671, and behind a Ju.87.

The King and Queen on a visit to Boulton Paul on 19th April 1940, in front of a model of the P.92, the four-cannon turret fighter then under development as the Defiant's replacement. The Chairman Lord Gorell is by Queen Elizabeth and the Managing Director, Herbert Strictland is explaining something to King George VI.

The Royal Party by a SAMM AB.15 pedestal mount for a 20mm Hispano cannon. Behind appear to be two Vulture engines, destined for the P.92 then on order.

A mock-up of the four-cannon turret for the Boulton Paul P.92, three prototypes of which were ordered.

The P.92/2 a half scale flying model of the P.92 built for Boulton Paul by Heston Aircraft for aerodynamic testing. The P.92 was cancelled before this ever flew.

A head-on view of the second Defiant Mk. II prototype, N1551, with a more powerful Merlin XX engine.

An aerial view of Wolverhampton Airport during the War. The four new hangers for No.28 EFTS are on the right, with the original Municipal hanger and club house nearer the camera. At the bottom of the picture are five blast pens cut into the hillside for parking Defiants.

The Type H twin cannon dorsal turret
under development during 1942.
Production of turrets was transferred to
Joseph Lucus with Boulton Paul
concentrating on turret development and
airframe production. The Type H was
cancelled just when the prototype was
nearing completion.

The BPA Type E four-gun tail turret
fitted to the Halifax and British
Liberators. A beautifully restored example
is shown here on the Yorkshire Air
Museum's rebuilt Halifax, on its 'roll-out'
in 1993.

Designed to Spec. F.18/40 to find a Defiant replacement, the P.96 was offered as here with a British Centaurus engine, 6 x 20mm cannon and a radar operator at the rear of a long canopy. It was also offered with a Type A gun turret and 2 or 4mm cannon, and also with a Sabre engine. A single engined aircraft was deemed to be not fast enough.

Boulton Paul's answer was the P.97 with two Sabres, as here, or two Centaurus redials. Again there was the option of a rear radar operator or a Type A turret, in which case the pilot operated the radar. In the event the Mosquito proved to be the Defiant's replacement.

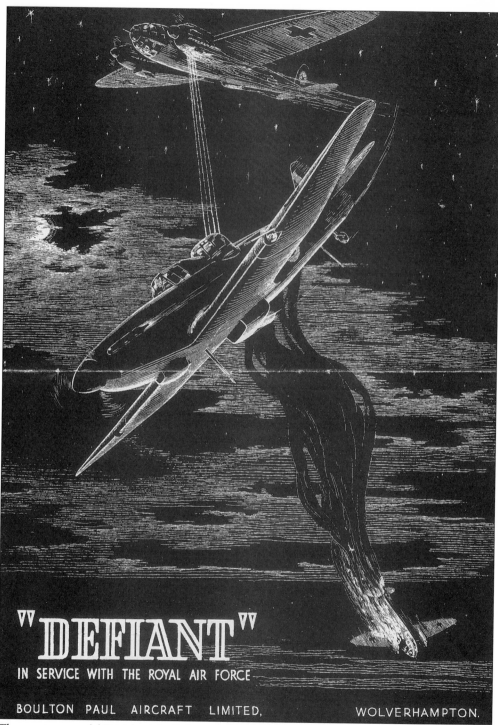

"DEFIANT"

IN SERVICE WITH THE ROYAL AIR FORCE

BOULTON PAUL AIRCRAFT LIMITED,   WOLVERHAMPTON.

The most successful British night fighter in the winter of 1940-41, at least one Defiant, N3378 of 255 Squadron shot down two Heinkels in one night as depicted in this advertisement. Fl. Lt. Trousdale and his gunner Sgt. Chunn shot down two in ten minutes on the 9th May 1941 over Humberside.

A night-fighter of No.264 Squadron, N1773, with a seemingly happy gunner. This aircraft later went to No.410 (Canadian) Squadron and then No.289 Army co-operation Squadron.

A No,96 Squadron Defiant, T.4052, coded 'ZJ H', at RAF Valley in 1941. This Defiant later went to No.60 OTU, then No.2 Air Gunners School, was then converted to a target tug and went to the Fleet Air Arm.

An aerial view of the factory in 1941. The Shropshire Union Canal alongside ran on an embankment, and the lock gate built either side can be seen. They were to prevent the factory flooding if a bomb breached the canal.

A drawing of a rear gun mounting designed for the Mosquito. Operated by the observer kneeling on his seat, the twin 0.5 in. machine guns were remotely controlled. The Mosquito proved fast enough to need no rear armament.

The French SAMM AB.15
powered mounting for a Hispano
20mm cannon tested both in an
Overstrand nose and in a Defiant
turret.

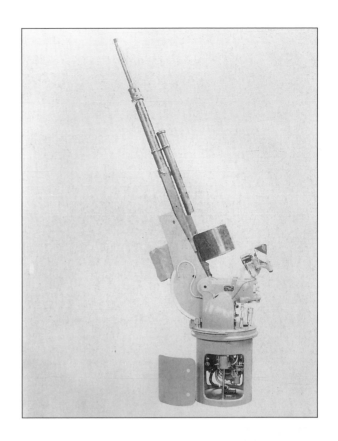

The turret school operated by the company. Turrets from the right, Type E in Halifax rear fuselage, dismantled Type A in turret stand, Type C Mk. I in mock-up Halifax nose, Type E, Type C Mk.II in Hudson rear fuselage, and a Type C behind the black board.

Numerous Defiants were converted to target tugs, and the last 140 were built new as TT.1s. This is a production example, DR972, which was delivered to the Fleet Air Arm and later sent to Cochin, India.

This is an artist's impression of the P.99 one of two Boulton Paul projects design to Spec. F.6/42 for a high performance fighter. The Hawker Fury was ordered to fulfil this requirement.

A Defiant target tug in Naval service at St Merryn. This was built as a fighter, served with No.456 (Australian) Squadron and No,288 Army Co-op. Squadron and was then converted to a target tug by Reid & Sigrist at Desford, who did most such conversions.

Defiant target tugs served in Britain, the Middle East, all over Africa and the Far East. This one has come to grief on Colombo racecourse.

The Defiant was replaced on the production lines by the Fairey Barracuda. This is a fuselage upside down in its assembly jig, pictured on 26th March 1942.

Almost three months later the same fuselage has now progressed to having its Merlin engine fitted, Note the blast walls running through the factory.

A total of 692 Barracudas were built, and later ones were assembled on the wheeled trolleys shown here. The first aircraft on the right is No.277, and on the left is 278.

The Minister of Aircraft Production, Sir Stafford Cripps visited the factor in 1942, and is the man in the glasses, alongside Ralph Beasley who was brought in by the Ministry from Armstrong Whitworth to oversee Barracuda production.

This is a finished Barracuda, wheeled from the factory on its trolley. It has just had its wings extended, and will shortly be lifted by crane so that its undercarriage can be fully lowered.

Sir Stafford Cripps chatting to one of the women workers, while Ralph Beasley waits patiently.

The completed Barracuda on the taxiway to the airfield, which was tarmaced during the War because of the heavy use imposed on it.

J.D. North showing Sir Stafford Cripps part of the Type A gun turret, the parts being laid out across the bench.

An early mock-up of the Type D twin 0.5 in. machine gun turret, complete with radar scanner. The final Type D turret which was fitted to the Lincoln was a less rounded shape. The Ministry was so impressed with this mock-up they told Boulton Paul to let Frazer-Nash designer see it.

Another attempt at a ventral turret, the Type R twin 0.303 in. turret with a periscope sight. This turret was tested in the Halifax and was largely satisfactory but was then cancelled and British heavy bombers remained vulnerable to attack from underneath.

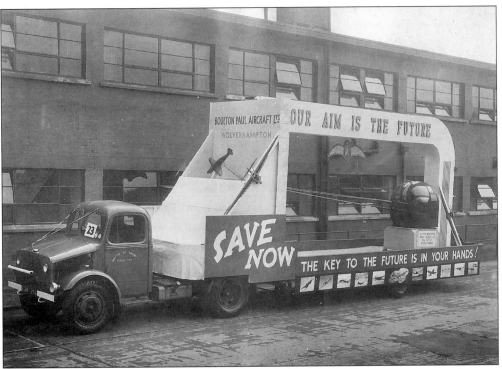

A Boulton Paul float outside the offices and featuring a Type E tail turret.

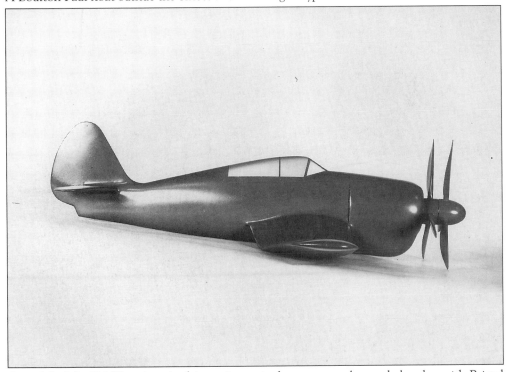

A model of the P.105 project, in this version a single seater naval torpedo bomber with Bristol Centaurus engine, dated 17th March 1944.

A mock-up of the Type S tail turret. This was one of a full set of turrets designed to American standards and specifications with 0.5 in. machine guns and intended for manufacture in America, a scheme which did not go ahead.

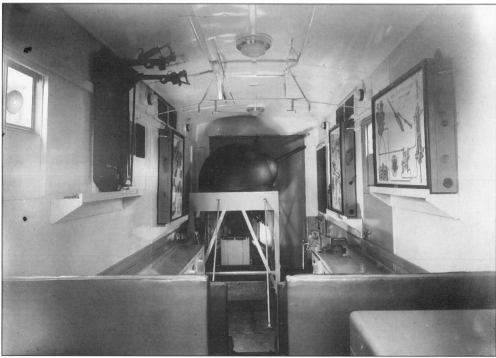

A Type F Lincoln nose turret in a mobile instructional truck. This turret, which began as the 'ideal Lancaster nose turret', was remotely controlled by the gunner sitting beneath in the bomb-aimer's position.

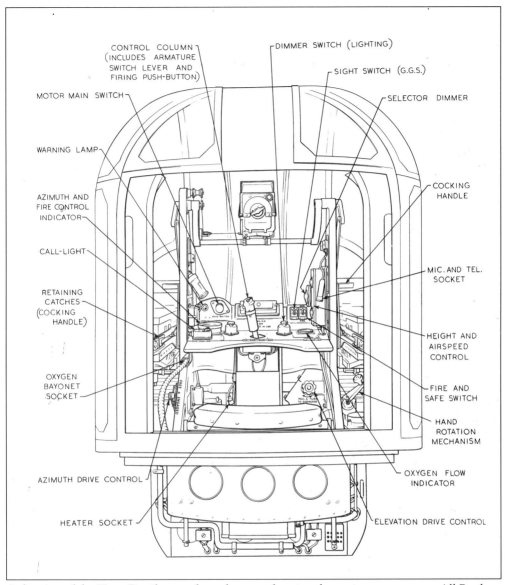

CONTROL COLUMN
(INCLUDES ARMATURE
SWITCH LEVER AND
FIRING PUSH-BUTTON)

DIMMER SWITCH (LIGHTING)

SIGHT SWITCH (G.G.S.)

MOTOR MAIN SWITCH

SELECTOR DIMMER

WARNING LAMP

COCKING
HANDLE

AZIMUTH AND
FIRE CONTROL
INDICATOR

CALL-LIGHT

MIC. AND TEL.
SOCKET

RETAINING
CATCHES
(COCKING
HANDLE)

HEIGHT AND
AIRSPEED
CONTROL

OXYGEN
BAYONET
SOCKET

FIRE AND
SAFE SWITCH

HAND
ROTATION
MECHANISM

AZIMUTH DRIVE CONTROL

OXYGEN FLOW
INDICATOR

HEATER SOCKET

ELEVATION DRIVE CONTROL

A drawing of the Type D tail turret from the rear, showing the major components. All Boulton Paul turrets were fundamentally the same.

The mock-up of part of a
remotely controlled fire-
control system for a heavy
bomber, featuring the Type
BC side barbette and a side
sighting station. The system
also included the Type BA
and BB dorsal and ventral
barbettes and an alternative
BD tail sighting station.

An internal view of the same
mock-up. This system was
similar to the one on the
Boeing B-29 bomber, but the
British abandoned the idea of
armament for their bombers.

112

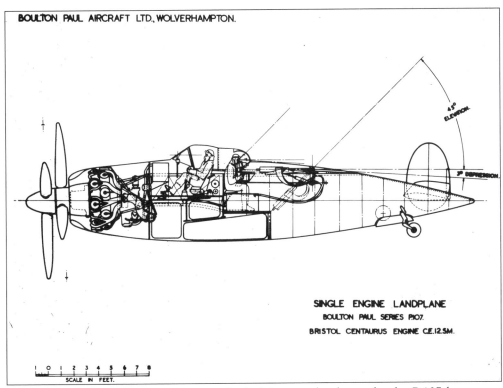

BOULTON PAUL AIRCRAFT LTD., WOLVERHAMPTON.

SINGLE ENGINE LANDPLANE
BOULTON PAUL SERIES P.107.
BRISTOL CENTAURUS ENGINE C.E.12.SM.

SCALE IN FEET.

Another Boulton Paul wartime project which did not make the grade, the P.107 long range fighter for the Pacific War.

The mock-up of Boulton Paul's P.108 proposal for Spec. T.7/45 for a new three-seater turbo-prop trainer, here envisaged with a Rolls-Royce Dart engine.

A Wellington bomber arriving at Pendeford after the War to be converted by Boulton Paul to a navigation trainer, one of 270 such conversions, The Wellington in the RAF Museum was one of these.

The Wellington were completely stripped and overhauled and fitted with a new nose fairing. Here an overhauled Hercules engine is being re-fitted.

The prototype P.108 Balliol, fitted with a Bristol Mercury engine for flight trails because the new turboprops were not ready. This was taken on 8th January 1947, the year of the very cold winter.

The Balliol prototype in the air, the second prototype, VL917, had the honour of being the World's first single-engined turboprop, powered by an Armstrong-Siddeley Mamba.

The Saro Princess flying boat for which Boulton Paul supplied the power-assisted controls to a Saunder-Roe design; the first PCUs built by the company.

The sad end of VL917; being flown by Chief Test Pilot Robin Lindsay Neale the propeller disced as he came into land, and hit the boundary fence. Note the jet-pipe in the starboard fuselage.

Balliol VL917 back in the Flight Shed. By this time it had already been decided to make production Balliols Merlin-powered, as there were large numbers of War-surplus Merlins in store. In the background is a Miles Martinet, RG907, at BPA for winch trails.

The third Balliol T.1 prototype VL935, being erected at Bitteswell, Armstrong-Siddeley's test airfield, where it made its early flights, having more room than Pendeford.

The first Balliol prototype, VL892 now re-engined with a Mamba, making it the third turboprop T.1. It also has the new sloping rear canopy of the production Balliol.

Three Balliols with different engines. Left to right: VW897, the Merlin-engined prototype T.2, VL935, Mamba-engined and VL892 with Mercury engine.

The final erection on the Balliol production lines in May 1952. WF989 in the background is the first production Balliol T.2.

Following the death of Robin Lindsay Neale in a Balliol crash, A.E. 'Ben' Gunn was seconded from his position on the Test Squadron at Boscombe Down and then appointed as Boulton Paul's new Chief Test Pilot.

The first production Balliol being handed over on 26th May 1952. Left to right: Jimmy Dalston (Production Superintendent), Geoff Kirkpartrick (AID Inspector), Geoffrey Haynes (Co. Secretary), Ralph Beasley (Production Director), unknown RAF officer, Ben Gunn (Chief Test Pilot) and Richard 'Dickie' Mancus (Assistant Test Pilot).

A Balliol with the full range of underwing armament available for training, 4 x rockets, 8 x practice bombs, 2 x underwing tanks. In addition there was a machine gun in the port wing and a gun camera in the other wing.

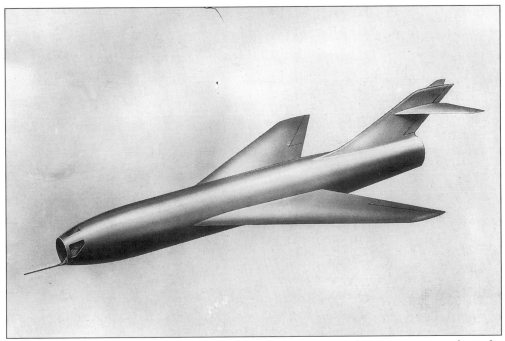

An artist's impression of the P.113 project for an experimental supersonic aircraft, to be powered either with an Avon or Sapphire engine. The pilot was sited within the air intake.

A pre-production Balliol, VR590, outside the flight shed and behind an elaborate mock-up of what Boulton Paul hoped would become the Balliol's replacement, the P.119.

The P.119 was an applied jet trainer of very attractive lines, offered either with a Nene or Derwent engine. The RAF ordered the Vampire T.11 instead.

The elaborate nature of the P.119 mock-up is illustrated by this feature which shows how the rear fuselage could be removed for complete access to the engine.

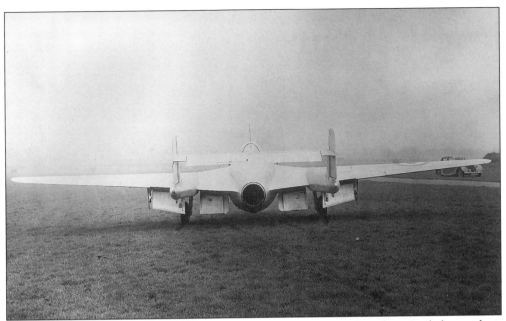

A Nene powered Vampire, TG276, at Pendeford for fitment of Boulton Paul designed air intakes and tail. It was one of the few jets ever to fly from Pendeford's grass runway.

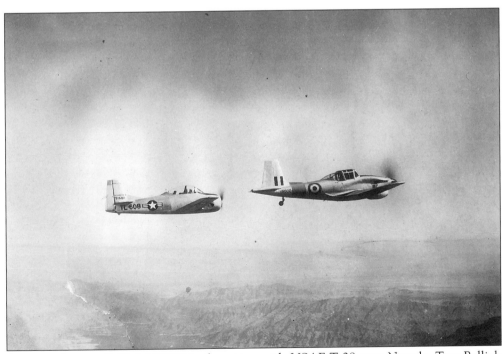

A pre-production Balliol, VR600 in formation with USAF T-28 over Nevada. Two Balliols went to America to take part in a USAF study of tandem versus side-by-side seating in trainers.

Three production Balliols in service with No.7 Flying Training School at Cottesmore. The RAF College Cranwell was the other main user of Balliols before the Vampire took over.

Boulton Paul's expanding Electronics Department created one of the World's first computers in the early 50s. It was nicknamed 'The Brain' in the factory.

The aggressive but attractive lines of the Balliol are well illustrated in this photograph, with the large chin radiator prominent.

An artist's impression of Boulton Paul's offering for the RAF's new basic jet trainer requirement, the P.124. The RAF ordered the Jet Provost instead.

The first of two experimental delta wing jets, the P.111 undergoing fuel flow tests in February 1950. The second, the P.120, can be seen taking shape under the P.111's wing-tip.

The P.111, VT935, in the air from Boscombe Down. It flew with three different wing-tips.

The P.111 on the ground at Boscombe Down, being prepared for a flight by Ben Gunn. The little delta contained some of Boulton Paul's first ever power assisted controls.

The 'stealth' Balliol, covered with experimental radar absorbing DX.3 material, in a RAF programme which later included the Canberra.

A Balliol ready for test, with the Rolls-Royce Rep., Joe Plant in Glasses. Joe came to Boulton Paul in January 1939 to work with the Defiant, then looked after the Merlins in Barracudas, and was still testing Merlins in Balliols in 1955. With him, left to right: Dickie Mancus, Keith Sedgewick and Peter Thomas.

Boulton Paul also built 30 Sea Balliol T.21s for the Fleet Air Arm, and this one is about to be delivered to the Junior Officer's Conversion Course at RNAS Ford, with Dickie Mancus and Ben Gunn in attendance.

Boulton Paul bought back the pre-production Balliol VR603 and registered it G-ANSF as their own demonstrator, painted maroon and cream.

A Sea Balliol prototype, converted from one of the Balliol pre-production aircraft landing on HMS *Illustrious* in December 1950.

Boulton Paul built the wings for the Supermarine Swift jet fighter, and the production line is shown here.

Boulton Paul's last production gun turret, the twin cannon Type N nose mounting for the Shackleton. Not strictly a turret as the guns only moved in elevation, and were for offensive not defensive purposes.

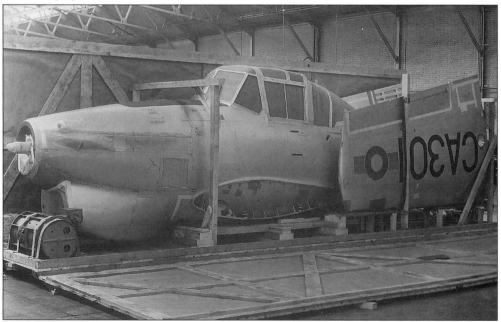

Twelve Balliols were sold to the Royal Ceylon Air Force, five new ones and seven second hand RAF examples. This is the first, CA 301 being packed for shipment to Ceylon in September 1953.

The P.111 was rebuilt, after a landing accident, with four air-brakes as shown here at Boscombe Down, to become the P.111A.

The Boulton Paul crew at Boscombe Down with the all-yellow P.111A. Left to right: Freddie Turner, Jack Wethington, -?-, Jack Perry, -?-, Ken Blakeley, -?-, -?-.

One of the annual Boulton Paul Apprentice photographs, this one being in 1958, with the Modifications Balliol as a back-drop.

From 1953 to 1965 Boulton Paul performed most of the major modifications on the English Electric Canberra, and used a new Flight Test Centre at Seighford, near Stafford. This B.2 has been transported to Pendeford by road.

The second of the experimental Boulton Paul deltas was the P.120, VT951, fitted with an all-moving tailplane. It is shown here at Boscombe Down where it made its first flight.

A second view of the P.120, featuring the swept tail. The first flight was made by Ben Gunn, with the aircraft still in its all-metal finish.

The P.120 was painted in an all-black colour scheme for an appearance in the 1952 Farnborough Air Show, but it was not to be, the in-flight failure of an elevon forced Ben Gunn to eject, and the P.120 crashed into Salisbury Plain.

Part of the Boulton Paul crew at Seighford in front of one of the many Canberras they worked on. Second on the left is Ben Gunn.

The Boulton Paul calendar for 1956 featuring every aircraft type they ever built. Interestingly it does not depict the P.10, tending to confirm that their first all-metal aircraft never did fly.

Boulton Paul used this Tay-powered Viscount to develop the World's first system of electrical signalling to all control surfaces, for which Dickie Mancus played a prominent part.

When retired from experimental flying the P.111A went here to the College of Aeronautics as an instructional airframe, for many years, later moving to the Midland Air Museum, Coventry Airport.

The first of the long-nose Canberras built by Boulton Paul, VN828, the B.1 prototype, was fitted with an elongated radome to test the GEC AI Mk. 18 radar, as well as an interdictor cockpit.

The future of Boulton Paul was to be in the design and manufacture of power controls, as illustrated here. The unit in the foreground appears to be fitted to the P.111/P.120.

Three
Dowty Boulton Paul Ltd

In 1961 Boulton Paul Aircraft merged with the Dowty Group, and became Dowty Boulton Paul Ltd, becoming an integral part of a manufacturing group specialising in the production of high technology aeronautical components.

Dowty Boulton Paul became a world leader in the design and manufacture of power controls and fly-by-wire systems, and extended its electro-hydraulic and electronic expertise into non-aviation spheres.

The Canberra and then Lightning modifications programme continued until 1965, when the Flight Test Centre at Seighford was closed down; and in 1971 Pendeford Airport also closed.

In the 1990s a Space Centre was opened producing propellant tanks, valves and other components for spacecrafts, and in 1991 the company began trading as Dowty Aerospace Wolverhampton. The Dowty Group was taken over by the TI Group in 1994.

J.D. North with his great friend George Dowty, and Mrs North. The photograph was taken in August 1967 and the presentation is to commemorate J.D. North's 50 years with the company.

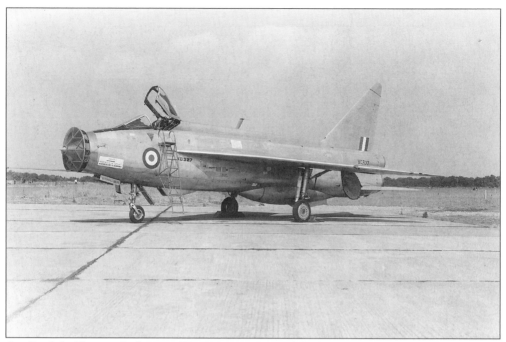

An English Electric Lightning F.I, XG327, at Seighford as part of the Lightning Mk.3 development programme mostly undertaken by Dowty Boulton Paul, following on their Canberra work.

A Lightning F.I, XG336, converted to a F.3 by Boulton Paul and awaiting its English Electric test pilot. Unlike the Canberra on which Dowty Boulton Paul test pilots did the test flying the Lightnings were flown by BAC pilots.

The last Vulcan II Power Control Unit with Dept. 561 personnel. Front row, left to right: R.G. Skidmore, N. Stewart, R. Hillback, G. Langley (Inspection Dept.), G. Broadhead (AID Rep.), L. Tongue (Works Mgr.), F. Hewitt (Production Director), Derek Hammond.

One of the last Canberra programmes worked on by Dowty Boulton Paul was the Nord AS.30 missile installation. This is Canberra B.15, WH967, at Seighford with AS.30s on the outboard pylons.

The two finalists in the final of the Interdepartmental Cricket K O, Drawing Office v Stress Publications.

One of the many aircraft fitted with Dowty Boulton Paul power-control units, the BAC-111, this one, N1541, being bound for Braniff Airway is shown at Wisley.

One of the first of the annual apprentice pictures without an aircraft as a backdrop; showing the changing nature of the company in 1963.

A Buccaneer flying over the aircraft carrier *Eagle*. The Buc had Dowty Boulton Paul PCUs on all three axes.

Perhaps the most prestigious contract was for Concorde, This is G-BSST, now on display at the Fleet Air Arm Museum. The company built up a huge amount of electrically signalled, or fly-by-wire experience with these aircraft.

A Concorde PCU being examined by D.J. Millard, Technical Director, and later Managing Director, on the left, Charles Kenmir, then Chief Engineer, and a naval officer who had come to examine the possibility of using them, or something similar in submarines!

Two of the great pioneers of aviation, on the left Fred Crocombe, formerly Chief designer of General Aircraft, and designer of the Beverley, later moving to Boulton Paul in the same capacity, and J.D. North.

The last Boulton Paul aircraft ever to fly, the Sea Balliol, WL732, in the year of its retirement, 1968, at the RAF Pageant, Abingdon. It is now in the Aerospace Museum, Cosford.

The First Aid Awards in 1962. Left to right: Denis Bolderstone, Jack Smith, Jack Careless, -?-, Renee Worrall, Sister Elaine Beebee, Geoffrey Haynes, J.D. North, -?-, Cliff Gandey, Sgt. Penzer, -?-.

Dowty Boulton Paul have produced PCUs for a number of foreign aircraft including the Hindustan HF-24 Marut supersonic fighter, which India did not in the end put in production.

The old drawing office in 1981 before new desks were installed. Dead centre is Ted Penny, whose father Sid was an AID Inspector at Boulton Paul for many years.

The Hunter T.7, XE531, fitted by Dowty Boulton Paul with quadruplex actuator packs as a further step in the development of fly-by-wire.

The ACT Jaguar, XX765, fitted by Dowty Boulton Paul with the World's first quadruplex flight control system with no mechanical back-up. FBW on the tail stands for fly-by-wire.

A drawing office presentation, left to right: Brian Tovell, -?-, -?-, Brain Huntbatch, Eric Paul, Ethel ?, -?-, Cyril Plimmer, Derek Whitehouse, Howard Howell, Alan Ellsmore, Ossie Burn, Dennis Keeling, Alf Walters, Ralph Tyler, Dave Cooper, Tony ?, Cecil Rose, Terry Herrington, Bill Cook, Sid Plafrey, Ray Hilton, Derek Mountney, Dave Lockley, John Willaims, John Grainger, Alan Bailey, Fred Morgan, Roy Cutler, Trevor Swann, Jim Ryder, Ed Albert, Keith Edwards, John Chambers, -?-, Ray Pearson, -?-, Lil Robinson, Marg Lloyd-Davies, Gladys Watkins, Joyce Bromme, Derek Nicholls. As the desk in the foreground says, 'Out of this World.'

The Airbus A.300, Dowty Aerospace Wolverhampton, supply a number of PCUs to several of the Airbus family of aircraft, as well as some of their Boeing rivals.

The British Aerospace EAP, the experimental aircraft which leads to the European Fighter Aircraft, a combat aircraft for the next Millennium. The EAP is at the leading edge of fly-by-wire technology and fitted with Dowty Aerospace Units.

The company has applied its electro-hydraulic expertise into many other areas besides aviation. This huge machine is a shipboard cable laying machine, one of many they have built.

In the 1980s, Dowty Boulton Paul designed the crane in the revolutionary Skyhook system for launching Harriers from ships without the need of flight decks, or indeed undercarriages on the aircraft.

Four

The Boulton Paul

Association

The Boulton Paul Association was formed in 1991 with the simple aim of preserving the long history of Boulton Paul Aircarft in all its forms. With a membership which includes former employees, Defiant aircrew and people who merely have an interest in West Midlands aviation and Boulton Paul in particular a number of projects have been initiated.

A large exhibition of the company's history has been created and new venues for it are actively sought. In a workshop provided by Dowty Boulton Paul Ltd the fuselage of a Balliol trainer is under restoration, and this has been joined by a growing collection of Defiants parts as the Association strives to put on display the company's most famous product in the town of its manufacture.

The Association has also set up the Staffordshire Aviation Archive, based on Boulton Paul's own substantial archives, and seeking to record the history of Staffordshire aviation in general and Boulton Paul in particular, and always seeking new material. This book, and a forthcoming video history of Boulton Paul are products of the Archive.

Jack Chambers, Print Room Supervisor in 1958. After forty seven years with Boulton Paul Aircraft he became founder member and first Chairman of the Boulton Paul Association in 1991. He died in September 1995 just after reading the proofs of his book on the Defiant.

Returning to work in the factory where they were all apprentices, Denis Bolderstone, Jack and Brain Holmes are shown constructing the exhibition 'Boulton (&) Paul Aircraft since 1915'.

David Chenery, Managing Director of Boulton & Paul Ltd, one of the sponsors of the exhibition, samples the cockpit of the centre-piece, the Sea Balliol, at the Aerospace Museum, Cosford. Jack Holmes stands on the wing.

Some of the team who erected the exhibition at Cosford, left to right: Denis Bolderstone, Reg Swift, Iain Whittingham, Jack Holmes, Harry Law, and on the wing of the Sea Balliol, WL732, Colin Penny and Ron Cooper.

Part of the exhibition featuring a model of the P.111A and a test specimen of the P.120 tail, on loan from the Midland Air Museum, Coventry. The Type D tail turret of the Avro Lincoln, behind, also featured.

The arrival, in May 1993, at Dowty Boulton Paul of the cockpit section of Balliols WN149 and WN534, presented to the Association by the Pennine Aviation Museum. On the left Ted and Colin Penny supervise their unloading.

Chairman Jack Chambers, smiling at the amount of work involved in restoring the cockpits, which had lain outside since being sold for scrap in 1957.

Restoration of the Balliols underway in a workshop provided by Dowty Aerospace. WN149 in the foreground is being rebuilt as a complete fuselage. WN534 was actually one of 30 Balliols built by Blackburn Aircraft at Brough.

The Airspeed Oxford V3388, for over 15 years Boulton Paul's company aircraft, G-AHTW, taken on an Association trip to Duxford.

The sole surviving complete Defiant N1671, in the RAF Museum at Hendon. Behind is the Wellington T.10, MF626, complete with the nose fairing built by Boulton Paul when they converted it to a navigation trainer in the late 40s.

The crash site of the Defiant N3378 of No.255 Squadron on Bleaklow Moor in the Peak District. This Defiant which had shot down three German aircraft during its career as a night fighter crashed in August 1941. The crew survived the crash but died of exposure while awaiting rescue.

Parts of Defiant N3378 being gathered in the Association's workshop. A project to put a second Defiant on display in the town where it was made. Parts have been collected from all over the country, from enthusiasts who brough them down from the Moor over the years.

Wolverhampton's Defiant on display for the first time, at the Cosford Air Show in 1995, including mock-up guns in the turret cupola, one of the few parts not to come from N3378.

Iain Whittingham, Colin Penny and Jack Holmes at work repairing the wing-tip of Cosford's Sea Balliol, damaged in gale-force winds while parked outside during hanger painting. Balliol WN149 makes progress behind.

Ben Gunn re-united with the P.111A delta at the Midland Air Museum, Coventry, during the making of an Association video on the history of Boulton Paul Aircraft.

Part of the Association's exhibition, on display for some time in the company's canteen, which has now closed. It has now been moved to a Visitor's Centre next door, incorporating the Association's workshop.

Some of the Association's restoration team, left to right, back row: Colin Penny, Dave Plant, Denis Bolderstone, Cyril Plimmer (now Chairman). Front row: Harry Law, Jack Holmes, Andy Simpson.

Further parts of Defiant N3378 arriving from the RAF Museum store at Cardington, where they had been in store since 1968, including the turret ring, propeller hub and windscreen.

Balliol WN149 with newly restored engine bearers attached to a new dummy firewall. Working on it are, left to right: Ray Simpson, Wilf Blick, David Jager (leaning on broom) and Harry Law.